Book Week Goes with a Bang!
Part 2

written by Jeremy Strong
illustrated by Ken Stott

Chapter One

Zak Gets a Nasty Surprise

Police cars, fire engines and ambulances raced to the accident on Story Street.

People came running from their houses to see
what had happened.
"Keep back!" warned the police. "There could
be a fire."

The fire brigade squirted foam over the tanker to smother any flames.

4

An ambulance arrived and two paramedics jumped out. They checked the tanker driver to see if he needed to go to hospital.

The firefighters went to the trapped lorry driver.
They used giant metal cutters to free him from
the cab.

The paramedics treated his cuts.

They put his head and neck in a special brace.

They put another brace round one leg.

Very carefully, they lifted him onto a stretcher and took him to the ambulance.

The ambulance raced off to the hospital.
The firefighters began to clear the road.

There was milk in the gutters. There were
squashed vegetables all over Story Street.
There were meat pies everywhere, and piles
of frozen chips and peas.

The driver of the tanker was taken into the school.
He was very shocked. "I don't know what
happened," he mumbled, over and over again.

The children were desperate to know what had
been going on. The teachers were doing their best
to keep them quiet.

14

Later, Mrs Turner called everyone into the hall.

"There's been a big accident," she told them, "but the two drivers are being well looked after. One of them is very shocked and is having a cup of tea in our staff room.

The other driver has a broken leg and he has been taken to hospital."

She told the children that the road was blocked.

"Your parents will still be able to take you home at the normal time though."

Mrs Turner looked at the other teachers. She was going to ask them to take their children back to class. But Zak Pieman had a different idea, and he whispered into Mrs Turner's ear. She nodded.

15

Zak fetched his drawing board, and he began
to draw a story for the children. They gave him
ideas and he drew them.

When they had finished the story, it was time
to go home.

The children walked silently past the accident, still in their fancy dress. They were too upset to talk.

The firefighters were sweeping up. A giant
breakdown truck arrived to drag away the tanker.

The teachers thanked Zak for his help and they went out to wave goodbye to him. Zak stared at the smashed tanker. He saw the lorry on its side. And then he saw the crushed car, half under the tanker.

It was **his** car!

Chapter Two

The Way Home

Zak was shocked. For a few moments he could not move.

"Are you all right?" asked Mrs Turner.

Zak swallowed and took a deep, deep breath.

"That's my car," he whispered.

Mrs Turner was shocked too.

"Oh dear, I am so sorry. What will you do?"

Zak shook his head. He had no idea. He was too upset to think.

"Perhaps you should talk to the police,"
Mrs Turner suggested.

"Yes, yes, of course," said Zak. He went over to
a policewoman.

"Poor man," said Mrs Turner. "Fancy coming
all this way and then having your car crushed
by a lorry."

"He looks awfully upset," said Miss Cherry.

"You wait for him out here," said Mrs Turner.

"Bring him in for a cup of tea when he's ready."

The breakdown truck lifted the lorry away from the crushed car. The firefighters used their hoses to wash away the milk and food.

Miss Cherry went and stood with Zak while he spoke to the policewoman. He was glad she was there, and they went back to school together.

They all sat down in the staff room. Zak was beginning to recover from his shock, and he even made a joke of it.

"If I wrote a story about this nobody would believe me."

Miss Cherry gazed at him. "What will you do now?"

"Well, the police said that they will sort out the car for me. Now I'll have to get home some other way. Is there a train station near here?"

"It's not far," said Mr Hopkins, who was still dressed as Peter Rabbit. "I can take you there in my ..."

"I'll take you!" said Miss Cherry loudly. "I have to go past the station on my way home," she added with a smile. Mr Hopkins was about to say that Miss Cherry didn't live anywhere near the station, but Mrs Turner stopped him.

Before they went, Zak and Miss Cherry took
another look at the accident.
"It's a good thing you weren't inside your car,"
she said softly, putting a hand on his arm.

Mrs Turner and the teachers were hiding in the staff room and peeping out of the window.
"Just look at that!" smiled Mrs Turner.

Miss Cherry drove Zak to the station. Sam was walking to the shop when Miss Cherry and Zak went past. Sam saw them and waved, but they didn't see her.

When Sam reached the shop she told Ravi
and Sunita.
"They were together! In Miss Cherry's car!"
Ravi grinned, but little Sunita looked cross.
She had other ideas.
"*I'm* going to marry Zak Pieman!" she insisted.